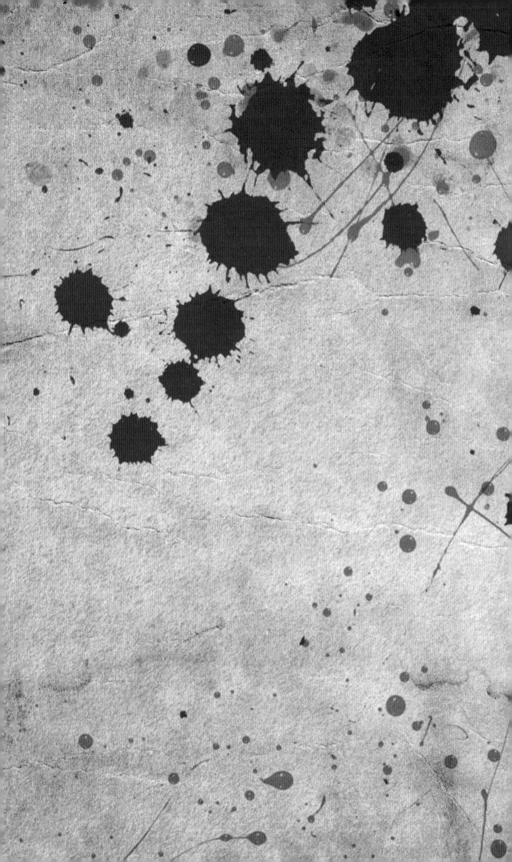

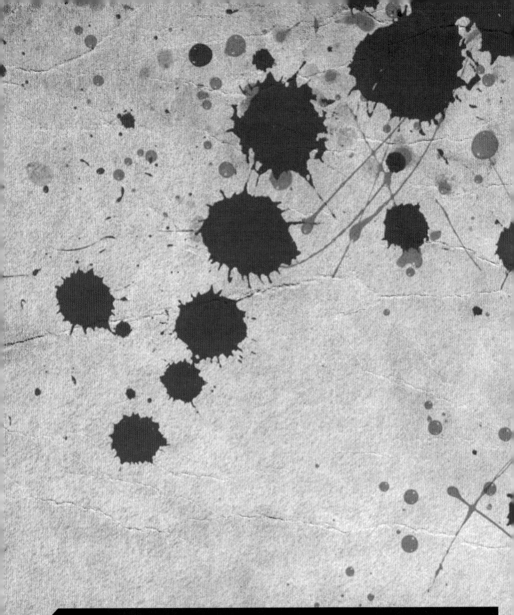

BOOM!
STUDIOS

Ross Richie - Chief Executive Officer
Matt Gagnon - Editor-in-Chief
Adam Fortier - VP-New Business
Wes Harris - VP-Publishing
Lance Kreiter - VP-Licensing & Merchandising
Chip Mosher - Marketing Director
Bryce Carlson - Managing Editor

Ian Brill - Editor
Dafna Pleban - Editor
Christopher Burns - Editor
Christopher Meyer - Editor
Shannon Watters - Assistant Editor
Eric Harburn - Assistant Editor
Adam Staffaroni - Assistant Editor

Brian Latimer - Lead Graphic Designer
Stephanie Gonzaga - Graphic Designer
Travis Beaty - Traffic Coordinator
Ivan Salazar - Marketing Manager
Devin Funches - Marketing Assistant
Brett Grinnell - Executive Assistant

WRITER: J. BARTON MITCHELL
ART BY: DEAN KOTZ

COLORS BY: DIGIKORE STUDIOS
LETTERER: MARSHALL DILLON
Issue #1
JAMES DASHIELL
Issue #2-4

EDITOR: MATT GAGNON
ASST. EDITOR: DAFNA PLEBAN

COVER: JEFFREY SPOKES
DESIGNER: ERIKA TERRIQUEZ

CHAPTER ONE

"Neither the angels in heaven above,
Nor the demons down under the sea,
Can ever dissever my soul from the soul
Of the beautiful Annabel Lee."
- *Annabel Lee*, Edgar Allan Poe

He knows what is written on the grave. More importantly, he knows what it contains. He has been here so many times...

And yet... he must see.

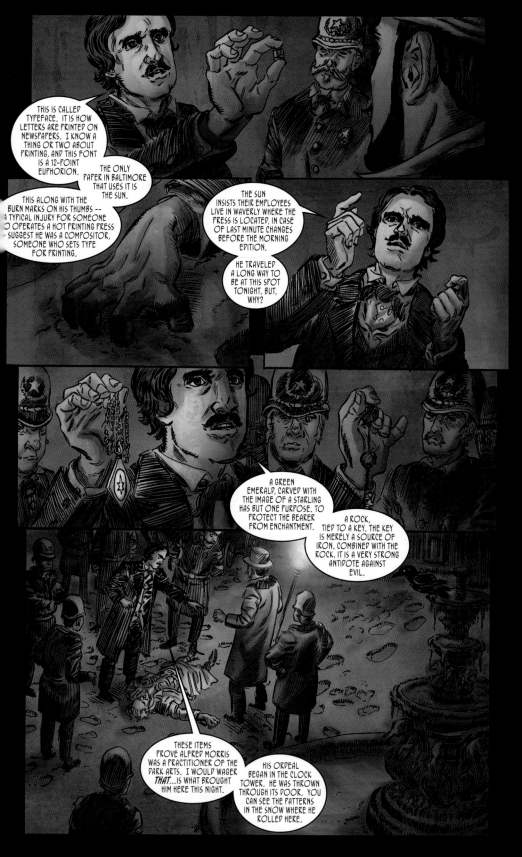

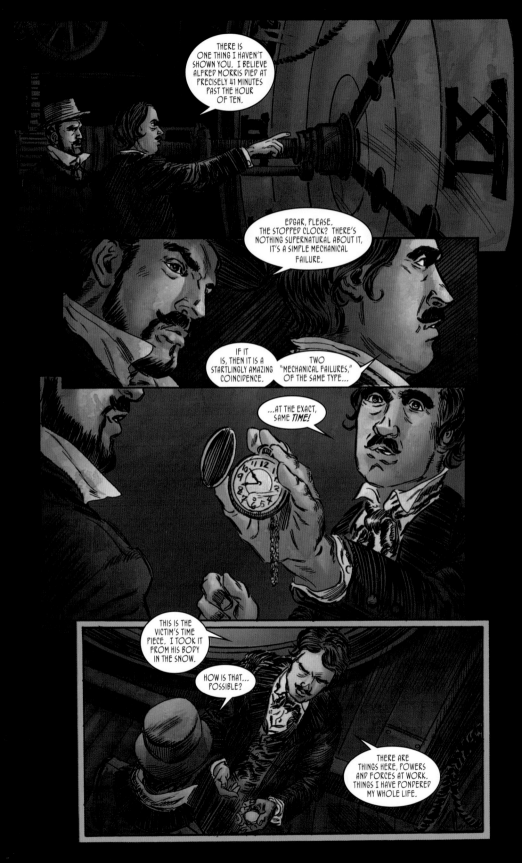

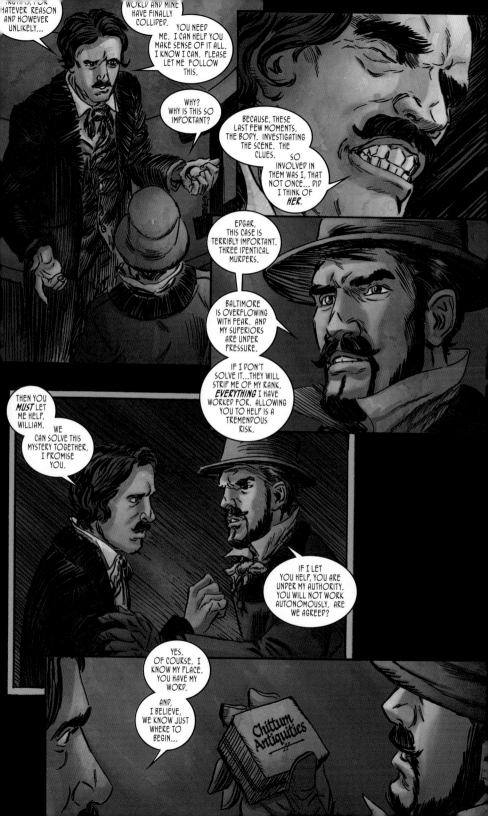

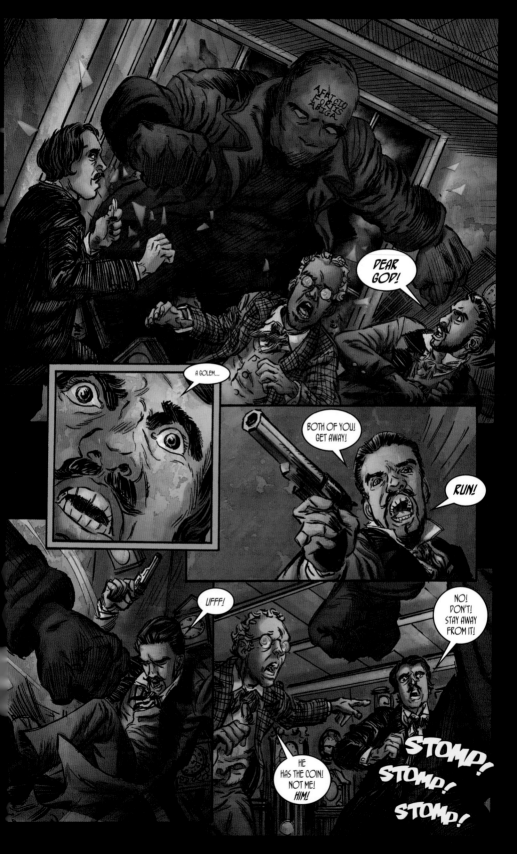

CHAPTER THREE

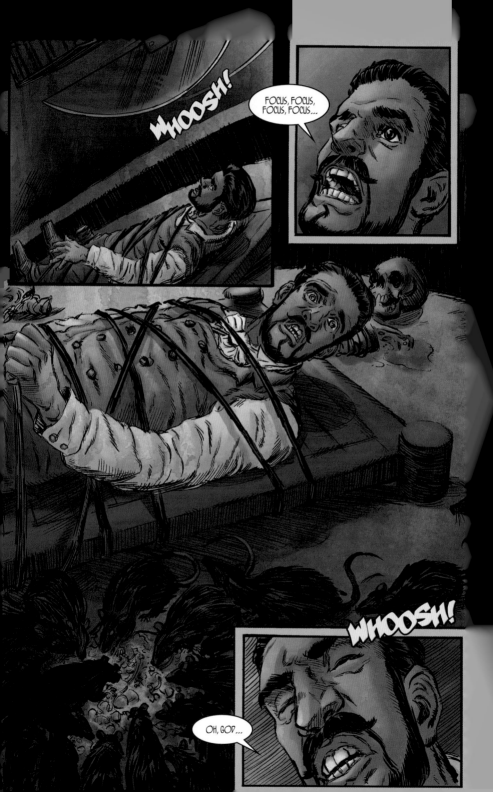

CHAPTER FOUR

In a dark dungeon beneath the House of Usher, the brothers Poe are in a great deal of trouble...

GRRRRRRRR

THUNK!

AARROOOOOOO

The horrible entity from beyond grabs Roderick Usher, holding him tight.

And all the while... it is changing.

Changing into the Necromancer's one, true fear...

AAAAAAAAHHH!

FREE AT LAST...

"I was a child and she was a child,
In this kingdom by the sea,
But we loved with a love that was more than love—
I and my Annabel Lee..."
- Annabel Lee, Edgar Allan Poe

COVER
GALLERY

COVER 1A: DECLAN SHALVEY / ANDREW DALHOUSE

COVER 1B: JEFFREY SPOKES

COVER 2A: DECLAN SHALVEY / DIGIKORE STUDIOS

COVER 3A: JEFFREY SPOKES

COVER 4A: JEFFREY SPOKES

COVER 4B: J.K. WOODWARD

EDGAR

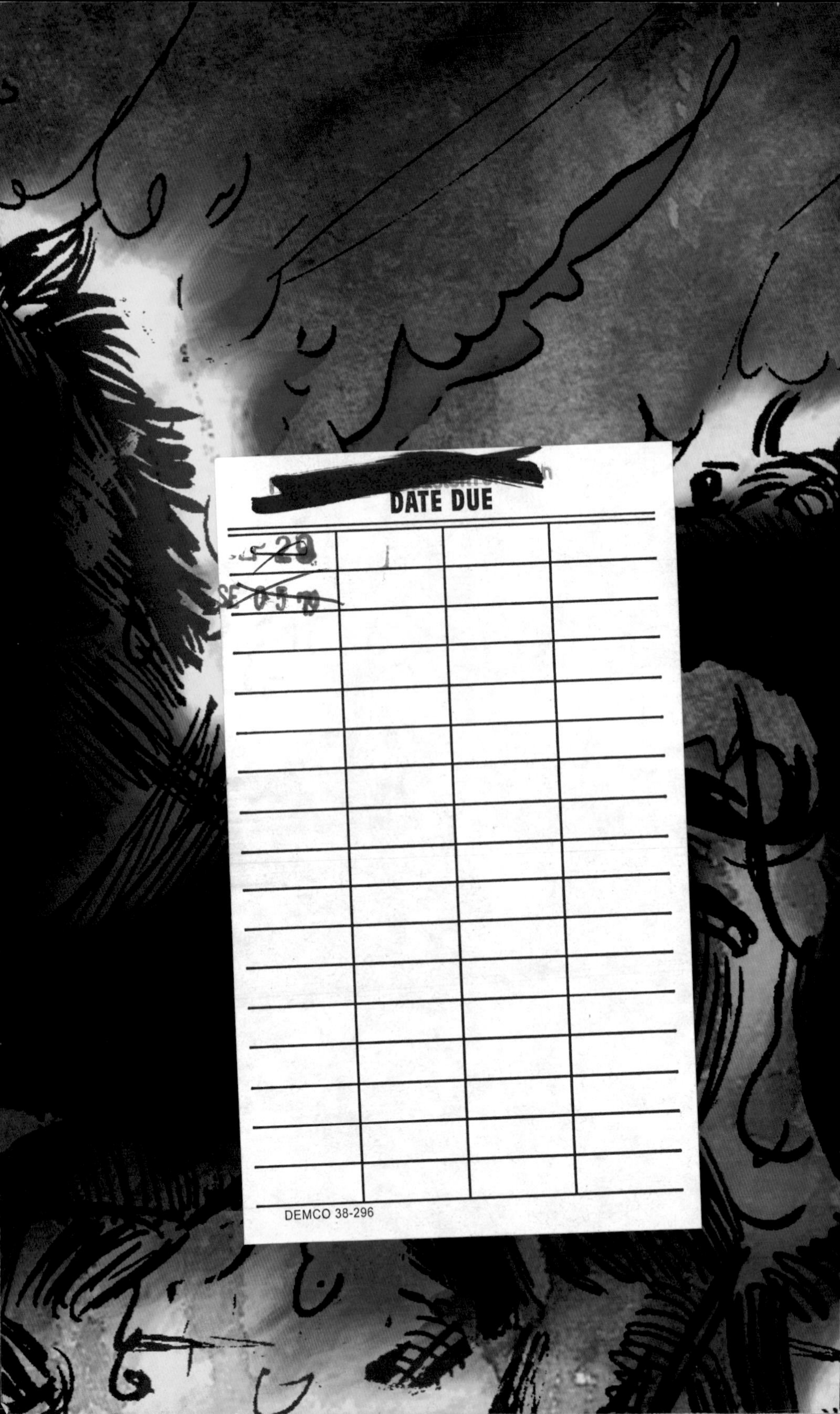